THE OUTER HEBRIDES

A LANDSCAPE FASHIONED BY GEOLOGY

Acknowledgements
Author: Kathryn Goodenough (BGS) and Jon Merritt (BGS)
Series editor: Alan McKirdy (SNH)

Photography: Niall Benvie 28 bottom; **British Geological Survey** 22; **Guy Edwardes/NHPA** 12; **Lorne Gill/SNH** front cover, back cover, frontispiece 4, 5, 7, 8 top, 8 bottom, 9, 10, 11, 14, 15, 18, 19, 21, 23 top, 23 inset, 24, 28 top, 29, 30, 31; **S Jonasson/FLPA** 16; **Peter Lewis/Alamy** 13 bottom; **David MacLennan** 13 top; **Patricia & Angus Macdonald/SNH** 6, 20, 25, 27.

Illustrations: British Geological Survey (image created using GEBCO Bathymetry data) 17; **Craig Ellery** 2, 3; **Clare Hewitt** 26; **Ian McIntosh** contents.

Fossil on page 11 courtesy of **Colin MacFadyen**.

Further copies of this book and other publications can be obtained from:
The Publications Section,
Scottish Natural Heritage,
Battleby, Redgorton, Perth PH1 3EW
Tel: 01738 458530 Fax: 01738 458613
E-mail: pubs@snh.gov.uk
www.snh.org.uk

Front cover image:
Traigh Iar, Horgabost, Isle of Harris
Back cover image:
Peatland lochan, Isle of Harris

THE OUTER HEBRIDES

A Landscape Fashioned by Geology

by

Kathryn Goodenough (BGS) and Jon Merritt (BGS)

A typical Outer Hebrides landscape, with white beaches backed by rocky hills

Contents

The Outer Hebrides form a 200 kilometre-long chain of islands off the north-west coast of Scotland, stretching from Lewis in the north to Berneray in the south, and including outliers such as St Kilda and the Shiant Isles. The different islands have an amazing variety of landscapes, from the peat-covered uplands of Lewis and the rocky mountains of South Harris, to the sweeping sandy beaches of Barra and the Uists and the sheer cliffs of St Kilda. The backbone of the Outer Hebrides is largely formed of ancient gneisses, some of the oldest rocks in Europe; in contrast, the Shiant Isles and St Kilda are geologically young, formed as the Atlantic began to open about 55 million years ago. Since that time, these islands have been shaped by the ceaseless pounding of the Atlantic waves, and by the action of ice, wind and rainwater, to form the remote and beautiful landscapes we see today.

The Outer Hebrides Through Time

QUATERNARY 2.6 million years ago to the present day		**11,500 years ago to the present time.** The climate warmed abruptly, and the glaciers melted for the last time. Relative sea level around the Outer Hebrides rose gradually. Forests colonised the islands, until humans began to clear the trees. Peat began to cover the landscape about 6,000 years ago. **12,500 to 11,500 years ago.** The climate was very cold again. Corrie glaciers probably returned to the Harris Hills, and freeze-thaw processes affected the landscape. **14,700 years ago.** The climate warmed rapidly with summer temperatures like those today, and the ice sheets melted away. **29,000 to 14,700 years ago.** During the last major glacial period, an ice sheet covered all but a few mountaintops in Harris and South Uist, extending at least 70 km westwards to the edge of the continental shelf. **Before 29,000 years ago.** There were prolonged cold glacial periods separated by shorter, warmer interludes.
NEOGENE 23 to 2.6 million years ago		Erosion occurred under warm, temperate conditions, cooling gradually until about 2.6 million years ago when the Ice Age began.
PALAEOGENE 65 to 23 million years ago		About 60 million years ago, volcanoes began to erupt along the west coast of Scotland. Magma was intruded into rocks and sediments close to the surface, forming sills and dykes. At deeper levels, magma accumulated in magma chambers such as that now exposed on St Kilda.
CRETACEOUS 145 to 65 million years ago		Warm, shallow seas covered most of Scotland, which was now around 45 degrees north.
JURASSIC 200 to 145 million years ago		The Minch basin was flooded by a shallow sea, in which animal life flourished, whilst dinosaurs roamed along the coast. Sediments deposited at this time occur on the Shiant Isles.
TRIASSIC 251 to 200 million years ago		Seasonal rivers flowed westwards across open plains depositing wide spreads of silts, sands and pebbly gravels.
PERMIAN 299 to 251 million years ago		By this time Scotland had drifted 10 to 20 degrees north of the equator and was again hot and dry, with sands and pebbles accumulating in valleys. Examples of these sedimentary rocks occur near Stornoway.
CARBONIFEROUS 359 to 299 million years ago		Scotland lay close to the equator and low-lying parts of the country were covered in tropical forests, from which the coal of central Scotland formed. The Outer Hebrides were part of a more upland region.
DEVONIAN 416 to 359 million years ago		Scotland was part of a vast, arid continent. As the mountains were eroded, layers of sand and pebbles were deposited across much of Scotland; rocks of this age are not seen on the Outer Hebrides, but may lie buried beneath the Minch.
SILURIAN 444 to 416 million years ago		Continents collided and the Caledonian mountains were uplifted. Blocks of the Earth's crust moved against each other along the Outer Hebrides Fault.
ORDOVICIAN 488 to 444 million years ago		To the south of the Outer Hebrides, the continents bearing England and Scotland moved towards each other as an ocean closed.
CAMBRIAN 542 to 488 million years ago		The Lewisian gneisses of the Outer Hebrides lay within a major continental mass, on the edges of which sediments were deposited. These sediments are only preserved in mainland Scotland.
PRECAMBRIAN Before 542 million years ago		The Lewisian gneisses were formed, and metamorphosed several times, during the Precambrian.

Brown bars indicate periods of time represented by the rocks and loose sediments seen in the Outer Hebrides.

Geological Map of The Outer Hebrides

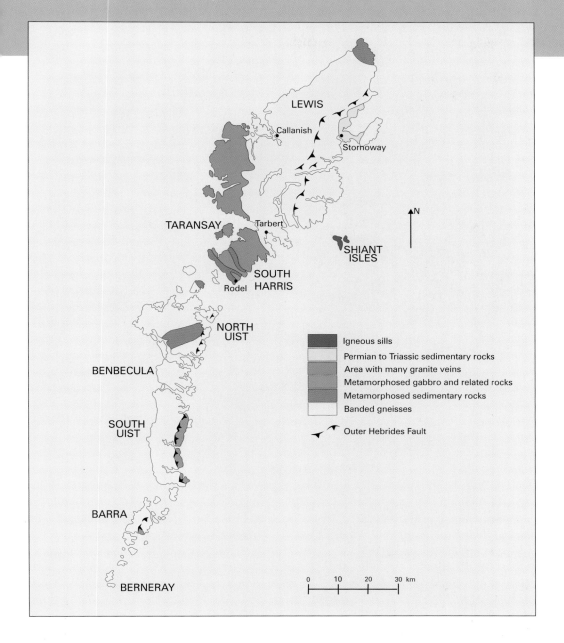

LEWIS

Callanish

Stornoway

TARANSAY

Tarbert

SHIANT
ISLES

SOUTH
HARRIS

Rodel

NORTH
UIST

BENBECULA

SOUTH
UIST

BARRA

BERNERAY

N

Igneous sills
Permian to Triassic sedimentary rocks
Area with many granite veins
Metamorphosed gabbro and related rocks
Metamorphosed sedimentary rocks
Banded gneisses

Outer Hebrides Fault

0   10   20   30 km

Among the Oldest Rocks in Europe

The main chain of the Outer Hebrides, from Berneray to Lewis, is made up of some of the oldest rocks in Europe. These rocks have been known as the 'Lewisian gneisses' since the late 19th century, and are named after the Isle of Lewis. They also occur in the north-western part of the Scottish mainland, between Skye and Cape Wrath.

Gneisses are metamorphic rocks – rocks that have been altered under increased temperature or pressure. In northern Scotland, the name 'Lewisian gneisses' is used to describe a complex series of rocks, which contains a record of several different geological events that occurred over a period of 1500 million years – about one third of the history of the Earth!

Banded Lewisian gneiss

Most of the gneisses that make up the Outer Hebrides started off as igneous rocks (rocks formed by the cooling and crystallisation of magma) nearly 3000 million years ago. The majority of these were types of granite, but some were more iron- and magnesium-rich rocks with less silica, called gabbros. Associated with these igneous rocks were small amounts of sedimentary rocks such as limestone and mudstone.

Most of the original features of these rocks were destroyed many millions of years later, when they were buried and heated deep within the Earth's crust, and metamorphosed. Metamorphism of the igneous rocks formed gneisses, which are characterised by alternating pale and dark bands, typically a few centimetres thick. The paler bands are commonly pale grey to pink in colour and are made up of crystals of quartz and feldspar,

whereas the darker bands are dark green to black and are largely made up of minerals called amphiboles. Metamorphism of the sedimentary rocks produced schists, which contain black, shiny flakes of biotite and reddish crystals of garnet; and marbles, which can be seen around Rodel on Harris.

Some time after this episode of metamorphism, around 2000 million years ago, rocks deep within the Earth were melted to produce more magma. Because this magma was hot, it was buoyant, and so rose upwards through cracks in the crust. However, it never reached the surface, and instead cooled in the cracks to form narrow, vertical sheets of igneous rock known as dykes. These dykes, which had the same type of chemical composition as gabbros, are generally called 'Scourie Dykes'.

Roots of the Mountains

The peak of Roineabhal is composed of anorthosite, which weathers to a pale grey colour. Scars of quarrying around Lingerabay can be seen in the foreground

The hills of the southernmost part of Harris, and Ben More and Hecla on South Uist, are formed from large masses of igneous rocks which are slightly younger than the Scourie dykes. Most of these igneous masses consist of gabbro, but the peak of Roineabhal and the outcrops around Lingerabay are made up of a particularly unusual type of igneous rock known as anorthosite, which is white in colour, and consists almost entirely of the mineral feldspar. Anorthosite is rare in Britain, but is very common on the Moon, where it makes up a large proportion of the lunar highlands!

The next important event in the history of the Lewisian gneisses was a second period of burial, heating and metamorphism, which occurred around 1700 million years ago and is known as the Laxfordian event. During this event, all the rocks, including the dykes and younger igneous rocks, were metamorphosed.

Sheets of hard, pink granite form sea stacks off the west coast of Lewis

This metamorphism did not create a new banding, but new minerals did grow – for instance, red crystals of garnet can be seen in some of the igneous rocks. The Scourie dykes are now made up of similar minerals to the dark bands in the gneisses, but we know that the dykes are younger because they clearly cut across the bands. This can be seen in many places across the Outer Hebrides; one of the best locations is at Leanish Point on Barra.

During the Laxfordian event, yet more magma was intruded into the gneisses of South Harris and western Lewis, to form veins and sheets of hard, pink granite. This granite is less easily eroded than the surrounding gneiss, and forms well-developed sea-stacks on the western side of the Uig Hills in Lewis.

The final event in the ancient history of the Outer Hebrides was the development of a structure called the Outer Hebrides Fault. This was a major fracture in the Earth's crust, along which rocks moved against each other. Movement may have begun during the Laxfordian event, but the fault has continued to move episodically through geological time. Deep beneath the Earth's surface, the Lewisian gneisses ground against each other along the fracture, and large amounts of friction were created, melting the rocks. The tiny amounts of melt created in this way were squeezed into cracks in the gneiss, where they rapidly cooled and solidified to form a network of black, glassy veins. This welded the rocks together, making them more resistant to erosion. Now, a line of low hills follows the Outer Hebrides Fault, from Heaval in Barra to Eaval in North Uist.

Man and the Lewisian

Blocks of gneiss in a dry-stone wall

The standing stones at Callanish

The Lewisian gneisses are hard rocks, not easily broken, yet over the years they have been worked by humans for a variety of reasons. Some of the most beautiful examples of the gneisses can be seen in the standing stones that are found all across the islands. The most famous site is undoubtedly that at Callanish on the Isle of Lewis, which was erected around 4000 years ago. Here, a central monolith is surrounded by a circle of 13 stones, with lines or avenues of stones leading away to north, south, east and west. The central, highest stone is about ten metres in height. All the stones are slabs of local gneiss, with their flat surfaces broadly parallel to the banding. On the rough-cut surfaces, the patterns in the gneiss can be clearly seen. Several other, smaller stone circles can be seen in the Callanish area, all cut in much the same way from local Lewisian gneiss.

With a lack of other available resources, the gneisses continued to be used as building stones on the Outer Hebrides for many years. The Iron Age brochs, including the famous Dun Carloway, were built of slabs of gneiss that had been split along the banding. In more recent times, these slabs were plundered from the brochs to build the blackhouses in which many Outer Hebrides residents lived until the mid-20th century. Stone for these houses was probably a mixture of beach cobbles, field boulders, and worked blocks of gneiss. It wasn't until Victorian times that imported stone began to be extensively used, for instance in building the town of Stornoway.

Most recently, stone from the Outer Hebrides has been in demand for road-building. In particular, the Roineabhal anorthosite is a valuable resource of light-coloured, durable and skid-resistant road surfacing aggregate, and so there have been proposals to open a superquarry in this area.

Raging Rivers and Shallow Seas

Conglomerates near Stornoway, made up of pebbles and sand deposited by rivers over 200 million years ago

Following their second metamorphism, the Lewisian gneisses remained within the centre of an ancient continent, far from zones of mountain building or volcanism. Thus, they preserve virtually no record of the ensuing hundreds of millions of years. One of the most important events in Scotland's geological history was the Caledonian Orogeny, which occurred about 500 to 400 million years ago, as the blocks of crust that would become modern-day Scotland, England, and Scandinavia collided. This huge tectonic episode led to the creation of a chain of mountains, stretching from North America across the Scottish Highlands to Scandinavia, and similar in scale to the present day Alps or even the Himalayas. However, the Outer Hebrides lay to the west of this mountain chain, and here the tectonic event was only recorded by some renewed movement along the Outer Hebrides Fault.

A beach cobble of Jurassic sedimentary rock from the Shiant Isles reveals a fossil ammonite

Following the Caledonian Orogeny, the crust of Scotland was lifted up so that the Lewisian gneisses were exposed at the surface. During the Permian and Triassic periods, around 300 to 200 million years ago, Scotland lay in the centre of a large continental mass, and had a hot, dry climate. The area that is now occupied by the Minch was a broad valley or basin, into which rivers flowed from the surrounding high ground. These rivers carried sand and pebbles, which were deposited along the valley margins, forming fan-shaped piles of sediment. Tiny particles of iron-rich material in the sand were exposed to the air and so became oxidised (rusted), giving the resulting rocks a red-brown colour. Most of the sedimentary rocks that were formed in this way are now beneath the sea, but remnants can be seen on land close to the coast around Stornoway.

At the start of the Jurassic period, some 200 million years ago, the Minch basin was flooded by a shallow sea. Sediments laid down in this sea were slowly compressed to form mudstones, sandstones and limestones. Small exposures of these can be seen today on the Shiant Isles, but they are also extensively exposed in northern Skye. Fossils in these rocks indicate that the Jurassic sea was teeming with life, including corals, oysters, other shelled creatures such as the coiled ammonites and bullet-like belemnites, and even plesiosaurs. Farther north, where the waters were deeper, muddy and organic-rich sediments were laid down. These sediments were the source of the oil that is currently being exploited in the area to the west of Shetland.

Erupting Volcanoes

The cliffs of the Shiant Isles are formed from thick sills of igneous rock

Around 60 million years ago, large-scale tectonic movements led to the crust of Scotland being stretched and thinned. The thinning was particularly intense along what is now the western coast of Scotland. At depth in the Earth, rocks melted to form magma, which rose up through fractures in the thinned crust. Where the magma reached the surface, volcanoes were formed; the extensive spreads of lava that were erupted from these volcanoes can be seen today on the islands of Skye and Mull.

However, much of the molten rock was destined never to reach the surface. Large amounts of magma were squeezed sideways into the layers of sediment that had been laid down on the seafloor during the Jurassic. This magma cooled and crystallised to form gently sloping, thick sheets of igneous rock, known as sills. The Shiant Isles, in the Minch, are almost entirely composed of sills that formed by cooling of a very magnesium-rich magma. The thickest sill is over 150 metres thick and is spectacularly exposed in the steep cliffs of the largest island, Garbh Eilean. These cliffs have impressive columnar structures, which formed as the magma cooled and crystallised. Solid rock occupies less volume than molten magma, and so the rock fractured into hexagonal columns; this is similar to the process that happens when hexagonal patterns form in a dried-up puddle, as the soil dries and shrinks. Today, these columns provide roosts for thousands of puffins, guillemots, fulmars and other birds in one of Britain's largest seabird colonies.

On the main chain of the Outer Hebrides, magma was not able to spread out through the hard and resistant Lewisian gneisses. In this area, some magma cooled in vertical cracks to form dykes. They are not always easy to distinguish from the much older Scourie dykes, although the younger dykes are characterised by very fine-grained margins where the magma chilled rapidly against colder rocks.

Close-up view of fractured outcrops of igneous rock on the Shiant Isles

Spectacular columns in the Shiant Isles cliffs

The Westernmost Islands

A steep-sided island in the St Kilda archipelago

Beneath the erupting volcanoes, magma was stored in huge underground magma chambers. Eventually, when the volcanoes ceased to erupt, this magma cooled slowly at depth in the Earth's crust, to form large masses of igneous rocks such as granite and gabbro. These large bodies of rock now form the mountains of Skye, Rum, Mull and Arran. Many similar bodies occur beneath the sea to the west of the Outer Hebrides, but only two of them are exposed as islands; St Kilda and Rockall.

St Kilda lies about 65 kilometres to the west of Benbecula, from where it is visible on a clear day. The archipelago consists of three main islands, plus a number of skerries and sea-stacks, and is a World Heritage Site for both its natural and cultural significance. It is composed entirely of igneous rocks that were formed at depth beneath a volcano around 55 million years ago. The volcano itself, and any lavas that may have been erupted from it, were eroded away many millions of years ago.

Similarly, the tiny islet of Rockall, which lies some 300 kilometres to the west of St Kilda, consists entirely of granite formed at depth beneath a volcano.

The western side of Hirta, the largest island of St Kilda, is composed of gabbro – a brown-weathering rock made up of large crystals of white plagioclase feldspar, brown olivine, and black pyroxene. In contrast, the eastern side, around the hill of Conachair, is composed of pale pink to white granite. In the area between, from Glen Bay to Village Bay, lie an unusual set of rocks that were formed by the mixing of two types of magma; the more iron-rich gabbroic magmas, and the more silica-rich, granitic magmas. These rocks are made up of dark, irregular blobs of gabbroic material surrounded by paler coloured granitic material.

The Opening Atlantic and the Start of the Ice Age

An active volcanic cone in Iceland

After the eruption of the Scottish volcanoes, the continental crust to the west of Scotland split completely and magma, rising up from deep in the Earth, was erupted to form new ocean floor. This was the birth of the North Atlantic Ocean, which continues to widen in the same way to this day. Modern-day volcanoes on Iceland are a continuation of the volcanic episode that started in Scotland.

Volcanic activity around the Outer Hebrides and St Kilda continued almost until 50 million years ago, and lavas poured out onto the seabed from a number of volcanoes. Some of these volcanoes now form seamounts – underwater peaks that rise more than 1,000 metres from the seafloor. One of these, Rosemary Bank, stands higher above the seafloor than Ben Nevis does above sea level! The thick lava flows cause significant problems for the companies searching for oil in the sedimentary rocks beneath the lavas.

A vertically-exaggerated image of the sea floor, looking NNE along the Rockall Trough, a deep-water basin west of Scotland. Water depths in the trough are around 2500 metres. On the left of the image is Rockall Bank, and on the right, the Hebrides Shelf. The three large seamounts in the centre of the Rockall Trough were once active volcanoes.

When the volcanic activity ceased, the exposed rocks on land were weathered and continually eroded under warm and humid conditions for over 45 million years. The eroded material washed off the land to be deposited as sediment on the seafloor.

The climate of Northern Europe cooled from about 7 million years ago when the Greenland ice sheet began to form. Significant ice sheets first advanced across the mid-latitude continents about 2.6 million years ago, but on the Outer Hebrides, evidence of early glaciations has been destroyed by the action of later ice. However, the presence of glacial sediments offshore shows that an extensive ice sheet covered Scotland some 440,000 years ago, reaching the margin of the continental shelf.

Since then, cold, glacial periods have been separated by much shorter, warmer interglacials every hundred thousand years or so, when the ice retreated. Drilling into the offshore sediments has shown that the area around the Outer Hebrides was glaciated at least three times. The last of these major glaciations was at its peak about 22,000 years ago, when an ice cap was centred over the remote mountains of southern Lewis and Harris. From there ice flowed radially outwards, fending off ice flowing from the mainland that crossed only the northernmost tip of Lewis. Curiously, across the Uists, the ice actually flowed eastwards towards the mainland, from an area of ice accumulation situated just off the western coasts of those islands. A vast expanse of ice flowed westwards from there for about 70 kilometres, reaching, but not engulfing St Kilda.

The Glacial Legacy

The Ice Age has left an indelible imprint on the landscape of the Outer Hebrides, creating much of its rugged and desolate beauty. Most of the glacial evidence we see today dates from the most recent major glaciation. The height of the upper surface of the ice cap at that time has been established on the mountaintops of Harris and South Uist, which protruded through the ice like 'nunataks' do today in Greenland. Areas of angular, frost-shattered blocks of rock, pinnacles and tors, which survived the last glaciation, have sharply defined boundaries with smooth, ice-scoured slopes lower down the mountainsides. These boundaries, called 'glacial trimlines', show that the ice surface stood no higher than about 650 metres above sea level around Clisham, and some hundred metres lower in the mountains of South Uist.

The direction of former ice flow can be established from whale-back shaped crags that have smooth but grooved ice-moulded surfaces and more jagged, plucked surfaces pointing towards where the ice was flowing. The source of the ice can also be determined from 'glacial erratics'. These may be large perched boulders of 'foreign' rock types, or stones within glacial deposits, that have been carried by the ice from distant sources. Erratics from the mainland (such as red sandstone and white quartzite) and from the floor of the Minch (including flint, chalk, limestone and chert) occur in older glacial deposits preserved within cracks and crevices, suggesting that the island chain was overridden by an ice sheet sourced on the mainland during an earlier glaciation.

View north-east over roches moutonnées close to the Laxdale River in Harris

A view north-west across Finsbay, South Harris, showing the iconic cnoc-and-lochan landscape

The ice flowed over watersheds, scoured away loose and weathered rocks, and over-deepened, widened and straightened pre-existing valleys, many of which may be described as fjords. Numerous ice-scoured basins are now filled with water or peat, surrounded by ice-moulded crags. This 'cnoc-and-lochan' type of landscape is best developed in South Harris, but also occurs along the eastern coasts of the Uists and Benbecula, where it contrasts sharply with the verdant pastures of the machair facing the Atlantic. In northern Lewis, the ice laid down smooth, thick, very gently undulating sheets of rubbly glacial material called till. The peatlands so characteristic of this area have formed on the till, which is extremely compact and clayey, and hence poorly drained.

Many arcuate, boulder-strewn ridges occur within the corries and glaciated valleys of the Harris Hills. These formed when sediment was deposited at the ice front as moraines, probably during a short-lived glaciation 12,500 to 11,500 years ago, known as the Loch Lomond Readvance. Freeze-thaw processes were prevalent at that time, with water freezing in cracks and shattering the rocks. On steep slopes, the loosened boulders and soil crept downhill to form distinctive lobes. Screes formed in the corries as frost-shattered rocks tumbled down from the cliffs.

Compared to the mainland there are relatively few features and deposits that can be attributed to glacial meltwater in the Outer Hebrides. Western Lewis is an exception, for the road to Uig passes through a spectacular, winding channel called Glen Valtos, which was carved out beneath the ice by eastward flowing meltwaters. In the vicinity of Carnish, ridges, mounds and terraces of sand and gravel that were deposited by the meltwater have provided an important source of natural aggregate on the island for many years. The main deposit originated as a delta built out into a lake that was dammed for a while by a mass of ice situated in Camus Uig and to the west. The lake probably drained through Glen Valtos, which acted as a 'glacial spillway'.

The winding meltwater channel of Glen Valtos

Ancient Beaches

Unlike in the Inner Hebrides, remnants of long abandoned beaches and wave-cut platforms are rare in the Outer Hebrides. This is because the Outer Hebrides are farther away from the former centre of ice accumulation in the western Highlands, and so have not risen (or 'rebounded') substantially since the weight of the ice was removed. Raised beaches are only seen along the north-western coast of Lewis, on the Eye Peninsula and on Barra. These partly cemented deposits of pebbly gravel generally lie between 10 and 14 metres above the present sea level, but their age and significance is uncertain. On Lewis they include rock-types derived from both the Minch and the mainland, suggesting that the sea redistributed deposits of an old, widespread glaciation. These ancient beach gravels are overlain by glacial material, and they lie on top of stony clays and rubble formed during Arctic conditions. This evidence tells us that the beach gravels formed prior to the last glaciation, and so are more than 30,000 years old. At Toa Galson the beach gravels rest on, and therefore are younger than, an organic deposit that formed in a cool, treeless environment following the last Interglacial period, possibly about 100,000 years ago. Towards the Butt of Lewis the ancient beach is overlain by a thick sequence of shelly glacial material, sand, gravel and mud, much of which was probably ripped up from the sea bed by ice flowing across the Minch from the mainland during the last glaciation.

After the Ice

Profound changes in the landscape were brought about 11,500 years ago by the sudden switch from a severe, dry Arctic climate to a relatively warm, wet one dominated by the Gulf Stream. Pollen grains and insect remains, contained within lake sediments and peat bogs, allow us to establish that a pioneer community of herbaceous plants soon began to colonise the thin, stony soils, followed by heather, juniper and grass. Birch scrubland was replaced by mixed birch, hazel and oak woodland by 8,000 years ago, when forests reached their greatest extent on the islands. The activities of Mesolithic Man then began to reduce the forest cover and extensive expansion of blanket peat began when the climate became cooler and wetter some 6,000 years ago. The islands were probably largely devoid of trees by the end of the Bronze Age, some 3,000 years ago, when peat was even more extensive than today.

Rising Seas

Towering cliffs on St Kilda

Around 11,500 years ago, the sea was over 50 metres below its present level and the coastline was well to the west of its present position, especially along the Uists. Global sea level then rose rapidly as the great continental ice sheets of the last Ice Age melted. By 6,000 years ago it was still about 20 metres lower than today, and it continues to rise slowly. During this time, stones and boulders derived from glacial deposits on the seafloor have been continuously ground and polished by beach processes. They have been rolled shorewards over many thousands of years to form the storm beach shingle that backs many of the shorelines today. The dazzling, creamy-white beaches are also partly derived from glacial deposits, but most of the sand consists of tiny shell fragments and an assortment of broken spines and other remains of marine animals and alga.

Away from the beaches the much-indented coastlines of the islands, particularly on the east coasts, are typical of a recently drowned landscape. High clifflines face the full rigours of the Atlantic Ocean and generally occur where there are deep waters offshore. Some of the highest and most dramatic clifflines in the British Isles may be found on St Kilda.

Beach shingle is particularly sought after for making concrete, tracks, road base and in foundations, but it is a non-sustainable resource. Little shingle is replenished from offshore, and its removal, coupled by an increase in the incidence of severe gales and high tides, is exacerbating coastal erosion. This is particularly problematic in the Uists, where the low-lying machair is protected behind a belt of vulnerable sand dunes.

View across Taransay to the sands of Luskentyre

The Machair

The coastal grasslands that back many of the long, white, sandy beaches along the western seaboard of the Outer Hebrides are particularly rare habitats in Europe, and are known as machair. In spring, rich carpets of flowers provide a stunning contrast with the bare, rugged rocks inland, especially in the Uists and Barra. Machair sand is largely composed of tiny shell fragments, which provide an ideal, well-drained, lime-rich soil to sustain rich grassland. Extreme winds blow beach sand inland to form belts of dunes that slowly become stabilised by marram grass. Finer-grained sand blows farther inland where it settles to create broad, flat, turf-covered plains. In severe gales, bare or loosely vegetated areas of sand lying above the water table can be blown away in hours to form deep, elliptical hollows that may take years to repair naturally.

Most machair areas include a mosaic of migrating dunes, long-stabilised dune fields and partially eroded plateaux, which record periodic changes that have occurred in net sand accumulation and removal by wind. These result from fluctuations in climate and changing influences of man and beast. Brackish lagoons, freshwater lochans and bogs associated with the machair provide a wealth of different habitats for plants, birds and other animals.

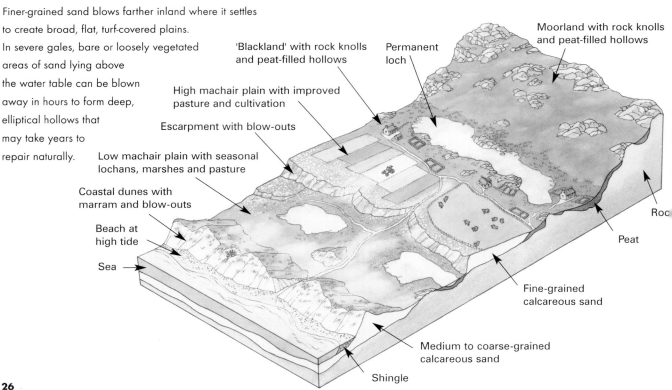

'Blackland' with rock knolls and peat-filled hollows

Permanent loch

Moorland with rock knolls and peat-filled hollows

High machair plain with improved pasture and cultivation

Escarpment with blow-outs

Low machair plain with seasonal lochans, marshes and pasture

Coastal dunes with marram and blow-outs

Beach at high tide

Sea

Roc

Peat

Fine-grained calcareous sand

Medium to coarse-grained calcareous sand

Shingle

Aerial view of machair landscape at Sollas and Malaclete, North Uist

Eroding sand dunes at Stilligarry, South Uist

Shell brash from Barra

Sand is traditionally taken from the beaches, dunes and machair for a range of building purposes and for spreading on acidic farmland inland. It is also used by crofters for bedding animals within byres. Uncontrolled commercial extraction from dunes and machair can exacerbate removal by wind and the blowing sand makes life very unpleasant for local communities. On Barra some beaches are particularly shelly and the shell 'brash' has been exported for many years, mainly for providing a decorative harling on buildings.

Machair flowers, Stilligarry, South Uist

The Landscape Today

Stacked peat cut from a bog in the centre of North Uist

The natural and cultural landscapes of the Outer Hebrides are particularly closely linked. This is especially so in regard to the natural richness and diversity of the machair, which would not have developed without human intervention over the millennia and will not be sustained unless traditional farming and crofting practices continue. In a land dominated by rock and bog and continually battered by the elements, the pattern of settlement on the islands has been primarily determined by the presence of soil to sustain pasture and provide arable land, and the proximity to beaches to harvest natural resources and food. Since the Bronze Age, most human occupation has been concentrated along the western seaboards, where calcareous sand has blown inland to cover the bare, ice-scoured rocks, providing a fragile foothold for man in an otherwise inhospitable landscape. Except for around some isolated sandy bays, settlements along the rocky and heavily indented eastern seaboards have largely grown up around natural deep-water harbours and jetties, providing essential links with the mainland.

The richness of the machair, particularly in the Uists, has allowed crofting land-use practices and way of life to persist when they have all but disappeared on the mainland. However, the importance of agriculture alone to the economy of the islands is dwindling in comparison to tourism and the subsidised conservation and management of a unique ecosystem and heritage of international importance.

The natural and cultural landscapes of the Outer Hebrides are heavily influenced by the cool, moist, maritime climate with its heavy rainfall, strong westerly winds and general absence of prolonged frost and snow. Countless generations of islanders have learned to live with the vagaries of the weather. For example, flooding of the low machair areas is inevitable for several months during the autumn and winter and droughts are common in the early summer. Beaches are periodically stripped of sand and shingle during winter storms to be slowly replenished later in the year. Now they face a more uncertain challenge brought about by rapidly changing climate, both natural and socio-economic. Difficult decisions must be faced in balancing conservation of the spectacular landscape with the development and mineral exploitation that is important for the economy of the islands.

Scottish Natural Heritage and the British Geological Survey

Scottish Natural Heritage is a government body. Its aim is to help people enjoy Scotland's natural heritage responsibly, understand it more fully and use it wisely so that it can be sustained for future generations.

Scottish Natural Heritage
Great Glen House, Leachkin Road
Inverness IV3 8NW

SCOTTISH NATURAL HERITAGE

The British Geological Survey maintains up-to-date knowledge of the geology of the UK and its continental shelf. It carries out surveys and geological research.
The Scottish Office of BGS is sited in Edinburgh. The office runs an advisory and information service, a geological library and a well-stocked geological bookshop.

British Geological Survey
Murchison House
West Mains Road
Edinburgh EH9 3LA

British Geological Survey
NATURAL ENVIRONMENT RESEARCH COUNCIL

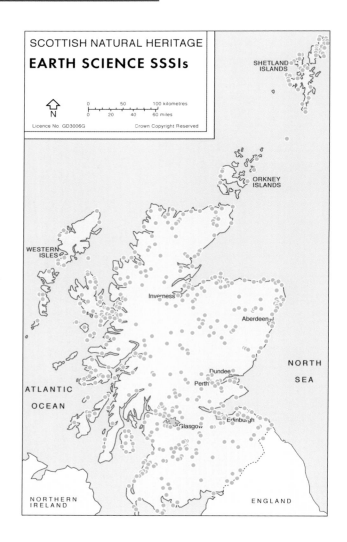

SCOTTISH NATURAL HERITAGE
EARTH SCIENCE SSSIs

N

0   50   100 kilometres
0   20   40   60 miles

Licence No. GD3006G   Crown Copyright Reserved

SHETLAND ISLANDS

ORKNEY ISLANDS

WESTERN ISLES

Inverness

Aberdeen

ATLANTIC OCEAN

Dundee
Perth

NORTH SEA

Glasgow   Edinburgh

NORTHERN IRELAND

ENGLAND

Remember the
Geological Code!

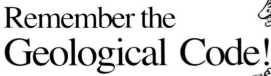

SCOTTISH
NATURAL
HERITAGE

No need to hammer indiscriminately!
Never collect from walls or buildings.

Keep collecting
to a minimum:
remove fossils, rocks
or minerals only
when essential for
serious study.
And remember to
refer good finds
to local
museums.

The leader of a field
party should ensure
that the spirit of the
code is upheld.

Always seek
permission before
entering
private
land.

No one has the right to "dig out" any site.
Try to leave the site as you found it!

Don't litter fields or roads with rock
fragments, and avoid disturbing plants or wildlife.

Back fill excavations where necessary to
avoid injury to people or animals.

Be considerate, and do not make things
more difficult or hazardous for others
coming after you.

Don't disfigure rock surfaces with brightly
painted numbers, symbols or clusters
of core-holes.

SAFETY FIRST!
✔ Wear protective goggles when hammering.
✔ Wear safety hats in quarries or below cliffs.
✔ Avoid loosening rocks on steep slopes.
✗ Do not get cut off by the tide.
✗ Do not enter old mine workings or cave systems.
✗ Do not interfere with machinery in quarries.

● Remember, you are one of several
hundred geologists visiting this area
every year — so your behaviour *does*
matter.
● Please observe the code, so that others
can also enjoy the great scenery, geology, and ecology here!

Published by Scottish Natural Heritage, 1996

Arran and the Clyde Islands

David McAdam & Steve Robertson

ISBN 1 85397 287 8 pbk 24pp £3.00

Ben Nevis and Glencoe

David Stephenson & Kathryn Goodenough

ISBN 978 1 85397 506 6 pbk 44pp £4.95

Cairngorms

John Gordon, Rachel Wignall, Ness Brazier, & Patricia Bruneau

ISBN 1 85397 455 2 pbk 52pp £4.95

East Lothian and the Borders

David McAdam & Phil Stone

ISBN 1 85397 242 8 pbk 26pp £3.00

Edinburgh and West Lothian

David McAdam

ISBN 1 85397 327 0 pbk 44pp £4.95

Fife and Tayside

Mike Browne, Alan McKirdy & David McAdam

ISBN 1 85397 110 3 pbk 36pp £3.95

Glen Roy

Douglas Peacock, John Gordon & Frank May

ISBN 1 85397 360 2 pbk 36pp £4.95

Loch Lomond to Stirling

Mike Browne & John Mendum

ISBN 1 85397 119 7 pbk 26pp £2.00

Mull and Iona

David Stephenson

ISBN 1 85397 423 4 pbk 44pp £4.95

Northwest Highlands

John Mendum, Jon Merritt & Alan McKirdy

ISBN 1 85397 139 1 pbk 52pp £6.95

Orkney and Shetland

Clive Auton, Terry Fletcher & David Gould

ISBN 1 85397 220 7 pbk 24pp £2.50

Rum and the Small Isles

Kathryn Goodenough & Tom Bradwell

ISBN 1 85397 370 2 pbk 48pp £5.95

Skye

David Stephenson & Jon Merritt

ISBN 1 85397 026 3 pbk 24pp £2.50

Scotland: the creation of its natural landscape

Alan McKirdy & Roger Crofts

ISBN 1 85397 004 2 pbk 64pp £7.50

Series Editor: Alan McKirdy (SNH)

Other books soon to be produced in the series include: Southwest Scotland, Northeast Scotland